MARRIAGE ON THE ROCK

GOD'S DESIGN FOR YOUR DREAM MARRIAGE

SMALL GROUP WORKBOOK

JIMMY EVANS

PO Box 59888 - Dallas, Texas 75229
972-953-0500 - www.marriagetoday.com

Marriage on the Rock Small Group Workbook with Leader's Notes

Based on the best-selling book *Marriage on the Rock* by Jimmy Evans, available from **MarriageToday**™ (www.marriagetoday.com)

Edited by Linda A. Anderson
Produced in association with Cenveo-Amarillo, TX.

MarriageToday™
PO Box 59888
Dallas, Texas 75229
972-953-0500
www.marriagetoday.com

All Scripture taken from *The New King James Bible* unless otherwise noted.

ISBN # 1-931585-11-3

Printed in the United States of America.

10   9   8   7   6   5   4   3

ABOUT THE SESSIONS

*Each session in this study is composed of the following categories: **Review**, **Get Started**, **Discover Truth**, **Relate & Communicate**, **Wrap It Up**, **Talk It Out**, and **Walk It Out**. A description of these categories follows.*

Review Each weekly session will start out with a time of Review.

Get Started (20 minutes) The purpose of the Get Started section is to help people get to know each other and get their minds and hearts ready to receive the topic of the session. The first point in Get Started is meant to be fun while introducing the group to the main idea. The ability to share fun with others is vital to building strong group dynamics. Each weekly session will start out with a time of review (except Session One). This is designed to provide accountability for the homework that is to be completed each week by couples between sessions.

Discover Truth (25 minutes) This is the main teaching of the session. In this part of the session, people will answer questions related to the topic of study and look into God's Word for insight. The Bible is used as the final authority on issues of life and marriage. God still speaks clearly and powerfully through His written word about conflicts and struggles faced by men and women throughout all the ages. We encourage you to bring a Bible with you to each session.

Relate & Communicate (30 minutes) Here couples will have a chance to interact with other couples and with each other to share personal insight and discoveries about themselves, each other and their relationship. Now is when true application of the principles taught during Discover Truth begins.

Wrap It Up (5 minutes) This segment serves to summarize the teaching and wind down the session in an appropriate fashion.

Talk It Out (10 minutes) Here the couples get a chance to discuss with each other and pray about the ideas presented in the session. It is also a time for couples to commit to setting a time to complete the homework for the week — the Walk It Out segment.

Walk It Out This is the time when real growth and healing can take place. It is designed to be a unique application time outside of the group meeting time, giving an opportunity for couples to make real change in their personal lives and in their marriages.

CONTENTS

Acknowledgments 7

Introduction 9

Session 1: The Most Important Issue in Marriage 11

Session 2: Covenant Relationship 17

Session 3: Principles of Positive Communication 23

Session 4: The Law of Priority 31

Session 5: The Law of Pursuit 39

Session 6: The Law of Possession 47

Session 7: The Law of Purity 55

Session 8: The Four Basic Needs of a Man 63

Session 9: The Four Basic Needs of a Woman 73

Session 10: Principles of Financial Success 81

Session 11: Sexual Fulfillment in Marriage 89

Session 12: Vow Renewal 97

Conclusion 101

Stay Connected 102

Resources 103

Leader's Notes 105

ACKNOWLEDGMENTS

I would like to acknowledge the many people who have contributed to the publication of this material as well as the success of the ministry of **MarriageToday**™. To the Elders of Trinity Fellowship Church, thank you. Words can't express the gratitude I feel for your unwavering support and commitment to me and to the call of God upon my life. Special appreciation goes to the Board of Directors of **MarriageToday**™. Your wisdom and leadership have been a source of strength and joy. To Rick and Linda Anderson, who took my words and put them into the form of a workbook for further study. And to an incredible staff who work tirelessly to create products and meet deadlines so that people are ministered to and lives are changed for God's glory. And to Karen, the love of my life, who has stood by me, loved me and prayed for me for over 38 years and who always trusted God to complete the work He had begun.

Thank you.

Jimmy Evans

Jimmy Evans

INTRODUCTION

Ahh! A wedding! The happy couple making vows before a room full of witnesses to be true to each other for a lifetime! They recite the traditional (and sometimes not so traditional) vows to have and to hold...from this day forward...to love, honor, and cherish...for better, for worse...in sickness and in health...until death do us part. It is perhaps the happiest day the couple has ever experienced. But now the wedding is over and the marriage begins. People with differing histories, expectations, goals, personalities and life perspectives now have to learn to live together. They find that "falling in love" is very different from building a good marriage. Most of these couples plan and prepare for every other aspect of their lives—buying a car, building a career, even going to the grocery store! But when it comes to knowing and planning what it takes to succeed in marriage, they are totally unprepared. But God has a plan. When He created you, He knew you needed a friend, a companion, a lover, a soul-mate. He wants you to succeed. In this study we begin the quest to understand God's plan for joyful unity in the marriage He intended for you.

Your part:

1. Commit to attending _____ weekly sessions. This class
   meets _____, _____ at _____.
   day of the week   time   location

2. Complete the reading and homework assignments prior to the meeting.

3. Don't share anything that would embarrass your spouse.

4. Be honest with yourself, others and God.

5. Keep this marriage group a safe place for healing by not sharing personal information that you learn in the group with anyone outside of the group.

Our part:

1. Provide biblical guidance to build a stronger marriage.

2. Maintain a positive, safe atmosphere for discussion and growth.

3. Commit to walk with you through a process of working through issues so that you can have the marriage of your dreams.

THE MOST IMPORTANT ISSUE IN MARRIAGE

The number one thing a couple can do for their marriage is make sure that each other has a true and deepening relationship with the Lord Jesus Christ.

GET STARTED

Who are you?

Take turns introducing yourselves and telling three things that best describe who you are.

Get connected...

- After everyone has had a chance to share, read Galatians 6:2 and Romans 12:15.

- How will staying connected with the other couples in this group help you on your way towards a better marriage?

- Pass your books around and have each couple write their names, phone numbers and e-mails, if possible, in the spaces provided at the end of the book, on page 102.

- When you have your book back, take a moment to read over the commitments for this group, found on page 9.

DISCOVER TRUTH

How you identify yourself has a great influence on your marriage. Every person is driven by the need to satisfy four deep soul needs — needs that define who they are.

1. What are some needs that you think all human beings have?

Reading for this session...

Read Chapters one and two of *Marriage on the Rock*

notes:

_____

_____

_____

_____

_____

_____

_____

_____

_____

_____

_____

_____

_____

_____

_____

_____

_____

_____

2. How would you define the four needs listed below?

   a) Acceptance

   b) Identity

   c) Security

   d) Purpose

3. Why do you think God created us with these needs?

4. What are the most common ways people seek to fulfill their deepest needs?

   a)

   b)

   c)

   d)

   e)

5. Read Proverbs 28:26, Jeremiah 17:5, and Proverbs 11:28. **What are the results if you expect others or things to meet these basic needs?**

   a) Inner security

   b) Ability to give

   c) Life atmosphere

   d) Unrealistic expectations

6. Read John 6:35. Why does Jesus compare Himself to the basic needs of eating and drinking?

Read Jeremiah 17:7-8, Psalm 125:1, and Proverbs 29:25. What are the results if you turn to Jesus to meet these needs?

a) Inner security

b) Ability to give

c) Life atmosphere

d) Realistic expectations

RELATE AND COMMUNICATE

1. Read again Proverbs 28:26, Jeremiah 17:5, and Proverbs 11:28. Share an example from your own life of the results of not seeking God to meet your inner needs.

2. Read again Jeremiah 17:7-8, Psalm 125:1, and Proverbs 29:25. Share a personal example of blessing as a result of trusting God to meet your inner needs.

3. Read John 4:1-42. What kind of woman do you think the woman described in this passage was?

4. What does this passage teach you about God's attitude towards people with failed marriages?

5.   What does this passage teach you about how marriages can be successful?

WRAP IT UP

Recognizing your dependence on anything or anyone other than Jesus can be difficult. Our dependence on other things slips up on us slowly and subtly.

Ask yourself these questions honestly, without answering out loud.

- Do I expect my spouse to make me happy?

- What expectations do I put on my spouse to meet needs that only God can meet?

- Is my inner joy, peace and fulfillment easily disrupted when things don't go the way I want, or when people don't behave the way I think they should?

- Am I confident that my life is built on knowing who I am in Jesus, and that no matter how people behave or how situations turn out, I am secure?

TALK IT OUT

Find a location away from other couples for privacy.

1.   Talk about ways to depend more on the Lord to meet your needs.

2.   Make a verbal commitment to each other to depend on the Lord, not your spouse, to meet your deepest needs.

3.   Ask each other for forgiveness for times when you have put unrealistic expectations upon your spouse that have resulted in hurt and division in your marriage.

4.   Conclude by praying for each other to have a deeper walk with the Lord and a greater dependence upon Him

5.   Before you leave this evening, set a time and place for you and your spouse to complete the homework session before we meet again.

OUR TIME

Date_____   Time _____

Place _____

WALK IT OUT

Before your time together, review chapters one and two in *Marriage on the Rock*. If either of you are not sure of where you stand in your personal relationship with Jesus Christ, please take the time to read Appendix I and II in *Marriage on the Rock*.

Begin by praying with each other and then share the following two things:

- Talk about the spiritual high point of your life.

- Tell your spouse one thing that you admire about his or her spiritual life.

Now spend a few minutes answering these questions individually.

1. Are there areas where you have sought fulfillment from someone or something other than God?

2. How has this impacted your marriage?

3. Have you had unrealistic expectations of your spouse in any area?

4. What have been the results of these expectations on your relationship with your spouse?

Share your insights from the above questions with your spouse. Be sure the focus stays on what you have done and not on what your spouse has done.

Below is a list of activities that can improve your relationship with God individually and as a couple.

Discuss which of these you would be willing to begin doing now or be willing to give more attention.

- Praying alone

- Praying as a couple

- Reading, studying and meditating on the Bible

- Reading devotional or theological books

- Attending church together

- Fasting

- Serving in the church

- Going on a retreat

- Entering into a discipleship or mentoring relationship

End by taking turns praying for God's help to keep your individual relationship with Him as the basis for your marriage.

For next week read chapter sixteen from *Marriage on the Rock.*

NOTES...

Read
CHApTer 16 $ SessionI

COVENANT RELATIONSHIP

A biblical understanding of covenant is foundational to understanding God's view of marriage and shapes our commitment to the marriage.

GET STARTED

Check It Out

To help you understand the importance of the homework assignments, take a moment to determine how many hours there are in a week. Of those hours, how many hours are you investing in your marriage during this group time each week? In each lesson you will get another tool to help your marriage thrive, and the homework you do will provide time to apply the tool to the building of your marriage. In a few sentences, tell how your homework went.

Two Becoming One

Wives, take a piece of pink clay, and husbands, take a piece of blue clay, and create something that represents you individually. Read Genesis 2:24. With your pieces of clay, demonstrate the idea of this verse by joining both pieces of clay together and making them one.

DISCOVER TRUTH

After mixing the two pieces of clay, attempt to separate the pieces of clay into individual pink and blue pieces again.

1. Why were you unable to separate the pieces?

SESSION 2

Reading for this session...

Read chapter sixteen from *Marriage on the Rock*.

notes:

2. How do you think this exercise parallels God's view of marriage?

3. God's view of marriage is based on covenant relationships. What would you say is the definition of *covenant*?

4. *Covenant* literally means "to cut, to sacrifice." Read Genesis 15:9-21. Why did God use the cut animals as a proof of His commitment to Abram?

5. Old Testament covenants involved the death of an animal as a portrayal of the idea "may it be for us like these animals if either of us breaks this agreement." Look at verse 17.

6. Jesus made a new covenant with us. What was sacrificed to establish the new covenant with us? See Ephesians 5:2. Him

7. We have been talking about sacrifice throughout this discussion, but what does sacrifice really mean? How would you say the world defines sacrifice?

8. To get a better idea of what sacrifice is meant to be, let's look at the sacrifice God made to establish His new covenant with us. Did God grudgingly send His Son? Did He send whatever was left over or extra? Or did He joyously send His very best because of His great love for us?

9. Our Western mindset is more accustomed to the concept of contract, rather than covenant. In terms of your rights, what does a contract provide?

10. A contract protects your rights and limits your responsibilities. A good example of this is a rental contract. On the other hand, a covenant limits rights and establishes responsibilities. What rights did Jesus give up and what responsibilities did He accept in the new covenant He established with us?

RELATE AND COMMUNICATE

1. Share an example of sacrifice in which someone gave his or her very best joyfully.

2. Share an example of personal rights that must be given up to establish a covenant in marriage.

Three key things for successful marriage: ① *Knowledge of God's word* ② *Commitment to the relationship* ③ *Daily personal discipline*

3. What was the motivation for God to send His Son as a sacrifice? How can that motivation be applied to the marriage covenant?

4. Covenant in marriage works on two levels — a covenant with God for your marriage and your covenant with each other. How can a covenant with God help your covenant with your spouse?

WRAP IT UP

Covenant requires a high level of self-sacrifice, but sacrifice is the basis for true love and intimacy.

- When both spouses mutually agree to sacrifice for one another, selfishness is put aside and selfish ambition is laid down.

- God is committed to be right here with you in your efforts to succeed in your marriage covenant.

- He wants you to have a strong, fulfilling marriage, and He will help you do what you cannot do in your own strength.

- Let's take a moment now to ask for His help and thank Him for His covenant commitment to you.

TALK IT OUT

Find a location away from other couples for privacy.

1. Briefly write down three or four things you appreciate about your spouse.

   1) Thoughtfulness of kind gestures on a daily basis to show he cares
   2) the really good full hugs he gives
   3) when he does something that he might not really want to
   4) the way he is my best friend and confides in me

2. Take turns sharing those things with each other.

20

3. Pray with your spouse, thanking God for giving you your mate, no matter what problems you are facing.

4. Before you leave this evening, set a time and place for you and your spouse to complete the homework session before we meet again.

OUR TIME

Date_____   *Time* _____

Place _____

WALK IT OUT

Before your time together, review chapter sixteen of *Marriage on the Rock*.

Begin by praying with your spouse and then share with each other the following:

- Your commitment to work through any troubles you are facing with God's help.

- That you would marry your spouse all over again.

Now spend a few minutes answering these questions individually:

1. What areas of my marriage are more like a contract than a covenant?

2. Where have I been focused on protecting my rights rather than on sacrificing for my spouse?

Share your insights from the previous questions with your spouse. Be sure the focus stays on what you have done and not on what your spouse has done.

As a couple, come up with a list of ways you will demonstrate your covenant commitment to each other during the next week.

For next week, read chapter seventeen in *Marriage on the Rock*.

NOTES...

PRINCIPLES OF POSITIVE COMMUNICATION

Good communication is not just important; it's essential to a marriage. Communication is the bridge that connects the hearts and lives of two people.

REVIEW

Share how a deeper commitment to covenant in your relationship has impacted you this week.

GET STARTED

Which Seed?

From the seeds set out by the leader, pick out a seed that will produce the following:

- Pumpkin
- Corn
- Watermelon
- Tomato
- Sunflower

Words can be very much like seeds. The type of seed you sow determines what crop you will reap. If you want to reap an atmosphere of love and praise in your marriage, what kind of words do you need to sow?

DISCOVER TRUTH

Read Proverbs 18:20–21 and Galatians 6:7. Words are incredibly powerful. God used words to create the universe and everything in it. Likewise, the atmosphere of our private worlds is created by words—the words spoken by us and those spoken to us by others.

1. What types of feelings or atmospheres can be created by words?

   Loving environments or Hostile /angry/hurt environment

SESSION 3

Reading for this session…

This session is based on chapter seventeen of *Marriage On the Rock*.

notes:

23

2. How are words like positive and negative seeds?

when you plant a bad seed in someone it roots and can spread negativity –
A good seed can root and continue positive growth

3. Communication is the most important tool for establishing spiritual, emotional, mental, and practical oneness. You simply cannot become intimate as a couple without proper communication.

   - Why would the area of communication be a good place for Satan to attempt to destroy your marriage?

   Because words can cause emotion and can lead to behavior that is resentful or accusatory or make someone withdraw & then allow their mind to be filled with evil thoughts

4. Good communication can only occur if we understand and accept the differences between men and women. A husband must understand and commit to meet his wife's need for deep, detailed communication. She needs the full stories with all the details, not just headline answers, so that she can feel connected to him and his world.

   - How would a woman's need for detailed information feel threatening to a man?

   He may feel he's being grilled or his authority is being questioned or not trusted

5. Likewise, a man needs a safe place where he is respected and honored for him to be able to communicate openly with his wife. It is the wife's responsibility to create that safe, secure atmosphere for her husband.

   - How would the wife sharing detailed personal information with family and friends create an unsafe environment for a man to share intimately?

   He would not want to open up if he's going to be ridiculed or hurt because of confessing or deep thought that are shared = No more trust

6. Unresolved conflict is another barrier to good communication. It is important that both spouses feel they can bring up problems to be discussed in order to find solutions.

   - What things might prevent a person from allowing his or her spouse to voice concerns about the relationship?

     1) Not Listening
     2) Fear of Disappointment or judgement or
     3) Fear they might want to end it
     4) Defensive Comments or Reactions

7. It is also important that problems be resolved quickly and not be allowed to become an area where Satan can accuse your spouse. If problems are not dealt with daily, positive emotions are killed and anger can become unmanageable.

   - How might Satan accuse your spouse if problems are not resolved quickly?

8. Two other keys to resolving conflict are:

   - Beginning your conversation with an affirmation of your spouse and an expression of your commitment to the marriage.

   - Listening carefully when your spouse is speaking—without interrupting or defending yourself.

   - What are some ways to communicate respect for what the other person is saying?

     Listening with eye Contact & Confirmation of understanding

9. Remember that the goal of your communication is to reach an agreement and to resolve the conflict—not for one person to "win" and the other to "lose." If you need to do so, agree to pray about the situation and come together again later for further discussion. Always end each conversation with tenderness and affection.

   - How could the location of the discussion have a bearing on the outcome of the conversation?

     Distractions or Other people

RELATE AND COMMUNICATE

1. Look again at the seeds brought by the leader. What words spoken in a marriage could be classified as negative seeds?

2. What words could be used as positive seeds in a marriage?

3. Give an example of an affirmation that one might use to begin a conversation about an issue that needs to be discussed.

4. Give examples of body language that would communicate genuine love and concern for your spouse while listening.

WRAP IT UP

Regardless of how much you read, discuss, or understand about good communication, it is the practice of good communication that is rewarding.

Do not hide your inner self from your spouse. The more you open up, becoming honest and vulnerable, the more you truly will know each other and the deeper your intimacy and love for one another will be.

TALK IT OUT

Find a location away from other couples for privacy.

1. Take a moment to reflect and write the answers to these questions:

    ■ What words did your spouse use during your courtship that affirmed and encouraged you?

    ■ What are some words from your mate that encourage and uplift you now (positive seeds)?

    ■ What are some words from your mate that bring you down and discourage you (negative seeds)?

2. Share what you have written with your spouse. Listen to what your spouse shares without interrupting or attempting to defend yourself. The goal of this exercise is to eliminate or uproot negative seeds from your marriage.

3. Pray with your spouse, asking God for His help in removing negative seeds from your marriage.

4. Before you leave this evening, set a time and place for you and your spouse to complete the homework session before we meet again.

OUR TIME

*Date*_____ *Time* _____

Place _____

WALK IT OUT

Before your time together, review chapter seventeen in *Marriage on the Rock.*

Begin by praying with your spouse and then share with each other the following:

- What types of comments and communication would you like to have from your spouse?

- What could you do to be a better listener to your spouse?

Now spend a few moments answering these questions individually:

1. What areas of my life or our marriage would I like to discuss with my spouse?

2. What behaviors interfere with good communication in our marriage?

Using the following technique, pick an issue to discuss with your spouse. One person will be the speaker/communicator for about five to ten minutes, while the other is the listener/learner. The speaker holds an inanimate object the entire time he or she speaks. Only the person holding the object is allowed to speak. The listener/learner practices listening skills. The listener/learner then repeats back to the speaker what he or she heard. At the conclusion of the exercise, the listener/learner is given the inanimate object and the roles are reversed.

1. While holding an inanimate object, the speaker talks without interruption from the listener, using non-threatening, non-accusatory language. For example: "I feel _____ when you do or say _____."

2. The listener/learner maintains good eye contact, positive body language, and refrains from making any comments. *(It is helpful to be able to hold hands with each other during this time.)*

3. The listener/learner repeats back what the speaker was trying to express, without judgment about what was said. *For example:* "What I heard you saying was ..."

4. Switch roles so the speaker/communicator now becomes the listener/learner.

Try to use this format of discussion three times this week.

For next week, read chapters three and twenty-three in *Marriage on the Rock*.

NOTES...

THE LAW
OF PRIORITY

A couple's marriage must be their top priority next
to their relationship with God.

REVIEW

Share briefly how you were impacted by the listening activities during the week.

GET STARTED

Hours of the Day...

Individually, fill in the blanks below reflecting your typical weekday. Estimate the amount of time you spend each day on the following activities: *NC*

- Sleeping _____ 7-8 HRS
- Cooking and eating _____ 2 HRS
- Driving _____ 15 MIN
- Working _____ 8 ½
- TV _____ 2 HRS
- Bible study and prayer _____ 15 min
- Chores _____ 15 min
- Time with spouse _____
- Time with children _____ N/A
- Exercise _____ 30 min
- Internet _____
- Other (please specify) _____

Reading for this session...

This session is based on chapters three and twenty-one of *Marriage on the Rock*.

notes:

_____

_____

_____

_____

_____

_____

_____

_____

_____

_____

_____

_____

_____

_____

_____

_____

_____

_____

Think for a moment about your answers to the "Hours of the Day" activity. What do your answers indicate are the most important things in your life? We will use this information during the "Relate & Communicate" section, and you will also use it during your homework for this week.

DISCOVER TRUTH

Two short verses—just 37 words—and they are essential to the success of the marriage relationship. Read Genesis 2:24–25.

1. How would you divide this verse into four sections?

2. Why do you think people miss the immense impact these verses have on marriages?

3. Four foundational laws for marriage are found within those two verses: *the Law of Priority, the Law of Pursuit, the Law of Possession, and the Law of Purity.* "For this cause a man shall leave his father and mother" is the first of these four laws, the Law of Priority. In most situations the most important relationship in a person's life prior to marriage is the relationship with his or her parents.

   - When a couple gets married, what needs to happen to the prior attitude of submission to parents?

4. Parents must still be honored and viewed as precious friends, but time with them after your marriage must not occupy top placement in your priorities. It is also important that you do not allow your parents to criticize your spouse.

   - How would you define *honoring parents?*

   - What is the difference between *honor* and *submission?*

5. What are some of the characteristics of a precious friendship?

6. Let's look at God's perspective on priorities. Read Exodus 20:1–4a. How would you define an idol? What are some idols in our culture?

7. Read Exodus 34:14. What are some things in your life that could make God jealous?

8. Legitimate jealousy is the righteous emotion that causes us to protect what is rightfully ours. There are forms of jealousy that are sinful and destructive-perversions of legitimate jealousy. Illegitimate jealousy is jealousy that comes from trying to get something that is not rightfully ours or trying in a sinful manner to hold on to something that is not ours.

9. If you allow anything or anyone, no matter how good or important, to take the time and energy that rightfully belongs to your spouse, you are violating God's design for marriage. As a result, your partner is going to experience legitimate jealousy. There are four ways we communicate and practically demonstrate our priorities. They are sacrifice, time, energy, and attitude. Define how each communicates priority.

RELATE AND COMMUNICATE

1. Look again at the activity on page 31. What surprises or disappoints you about the results of your answers?

2. In what ways could you show honor to each of your parents without allowing their improper influence over your marriage?

3. How could you communicate valued friendship to each of your parents without allowing improper priorities?

4. Give an example of legitimate jealousy.

5. Give an example of how you communicate priority to your spouse in each of these four areas:

   - *Sacrifice*

   - *Time*

   - *Energy*

   - *Attitude*

WRAP IT UP

Listen carefully to the warning signals from your spouse about feeling violated by other things or other people invading your priorities. As you commit to establishing and protecting the proper priorities of your marriage, you will find there are frequent challenges. Keep in mind, however, the awesome rewards you will reap.

Take a moment of quiet reflection and thank God for revealing the importance of right priorities. Ask Him to show you where you've let things get out of order and how to put them back into their proper place of priority.

TALK IT OUT

Find a location away from other couples for privacy.

1. Write down the areas in which you feel your mate is doing the best at showing how important your marriage is: sacrifice, time, energy or attitude.

2. Share those things with your spouse.

3. Pray with your spouse, asking for God's help in setting your marriage as your highest earthly priority and in learning how to communicate that priority effectively to your spouse.

4. Before you leave this evening, set a time and place for you and your spouse to complete the homework session before we meet again.

OUR TIME

*Date*_____ *Time* _____

Place _____

WALK IT OUT

Before your time together, review chapter three in *Marriage on the Rock.*

Begin by praying with each other and reviewing the "Hours of the Day" activity you completed at the beginning of this session. Discuss with each other the following:

- Besides your parents, what else have you "left" for the sake of your marriage? In other words, what other things that you value have you made secondary to your marriage?

- Identify three things that might be competing for your time and energy as a top priority over your spouse.

Now spend a few minutes answering these questions individually.

1. What things make you feel special and valued by your spouse?

2. What traditions to promote correct priorities in your marriage can you try to adopt? Be creative, but also realistic. Review the following suggestions for ideas:

- Each year on your anniversary, return to where you spent your wedding night.

- Have a "date night" every week.

- One afternoon each week work together on a scrapbook of the past year.

- Spend the first four minutes of the day and the last four minutes of the day in positive, loving conversation alone with your spouse and away from distraction.

- Make new "Hours of the Day" charts, like the one on page 31, reflecting the priorities you would like to maintain. Keep it in a handy location where you can review it often for a "check-up."

Share your insights from the above questions with your spouse and come up with at least one new tradition or adjustment to your schedule that will begin to move you towards correct priorities.

For next week, read chapter four in *Marriage on the Rock*.

NOTES...

THE LAW
OF PURSUIT

The quality of your marriage is determined by how hard you work on it.

REVIEW

Share the new tradition or adjustment to your schedule that you agreed upon during your homework time. If you were able to implement this change or activity, share the results.

GET STARTED

Remember When?

Think about the time when you met your spouse. What was the most extravagant thing you did to pursue the relationship? What was the most memorable thing your spouse did in pursuit of you?

DISCOVER TRUTH

The second foundational law of marriage is the Law of Pursuit. It is found in the second part of Genesis 2:24, "...and shall cleave to his wife."

1. What do you think is the meaning of the word *cleave*?

Reading for this session...

This session is based on chapter four of *Marriage on the Rock*.

notes:

2. Because cleave actually means to *"pursue with great energy and to cling to something zealously,"* God is commanding you to zealously pursue your spouse and to energetically cling to him or her as long as you both shall live. Our view of marriage, however, is often skewed by Hollywood romanticism and myths. One of these myths is: "If I marry the right person, I will not have to work at the relationship to stay in love—it will just happen automatically."

   ■ What is the false conclusion arrived at by a person who believes this myth? In other words, "If I have to work at the relationship, I must have ..."

3. What other marriage misconceptions can you think of?

4. Like muscles, relationships need exercise to stay strong. You had a passion for each other when you first met and you pursued each other with time and effort. It was an exciting time and you both felt special. Over time, people sometimes take marriage for granted and stop working on the relationship. Complacency then creeps into the marriage. God has given us a plan for renewing passion and displacing complacency. Read Revelation 2:5.

   ■ Why would "remembering" be a good first step to overcoming complacency?

5. According to this verse, what would be the second step to renewing passion and displacing complacency?

6. What is the definition of *repent*?

7. Again, from the above verse, what would be the third step to renewing passion?

Working at the relationship is the thing that rekindles passion. Do not wait on passion to drive your actions. Instead, do again the things you once did and passion will follow. Remember back to the early part of your courtship—when you first noticed and began to pursue each other. Those are the types of things that you begin to "re-do."

RELATE AND COMMUNICATE
1. Think again about the most extravagant thing that you used to do to pursue your mate. If that passion has slipped away, how can you regain it?

2. What myths have you believed about marriage?

3. Give an example of how a couple could work on the "remembering" step of renewing passion.

4. Give some examples of ways to "do the deeds you did at first" in your relationship.

WRAP IT UP

When you make the decision to pursue your spouse with energy and diligence, you will find it is a labor of love—not hard, grueling work.

You will experience the wonderful truth that marriage gets stronger and more satisfying every day when you do it God's way. Read Proverbs 14:23.

TALK IT OUT

Find a location away from other couples for privacy.

1. Take a moment to reflect and write the answers to these questions:

    ■ Have you continued to pursue your spouse the way you once did?

- Do you need to rekindle your love for your spouse?

2. Share the answers from the above questions with your spouse, and if necessary repent and commit to renewing your pursuit of each other.

3. Pray with your spouse, asking God to help you remember, repent and do the deeds you did at first.

4. Before you leave this evening, set a time and place for you and your spouse to complete the homework session before we meet again.

OUR TIME

*Date*_____ *Time* _____

Place _____

WALK IT OUT

Before your time together, review chapter four in *Marriage on the Rock.*

Begin by praying with each other and then share the following:

- What was the first thing that attracted you to me?

- What are some ways that I pursued you when we were dating?

■ What can I do to make you feel I am pursuing you now?

Now spend a few minutes answering these questions individually.

1. What would you like your spouse to do to show you that he or she is pursuing you in love?

2. Make a list of ways you can start to pursue one another. Here are some thoughts to get you started.

    ■ Call one another during the day just to talk.

    ■ Write each other notes of encouragement.

    ■ Write letters to each other when you are apart.

    ■ Give gifts without an occasion.

    ■ Surprise each other with a special date.

    ■ Set aside special time for one another on your calendar.

Share your insights from the above questions with your spouse. Choose several things you will do this next week to pursue your spouse.

For next week, read chapter five in *Marriage on the Rock*.

NOTES...

THE LAW OF POSSESSION

Sun 6pm

God designed marriage to be co-owned and co-administered by both spouses.

REVIEW

Share how you felt this week as you and your spouse practiced pursuing each other in love.

? N/A

GET STARTED

Whose Is It?

Make a list of your five most important possessions. Share the top one with the group.

- Pictures
- Rings & cross & locket
- Phone

DISCOVER TRUTH

The third foundational law of marriage is the Law of Possession. It is based on the last part of Genesis 2:24, "...and they shall become one flesh."

1. Beyond sexual intercourse, what else does becoming one flesh involve?

   TRUST AND INTIMACY — Sharing of the Soul

SESSION 6

Reading for this session...

This session is based on chapter five of *Marriage on the Rock*.

notes:

2. The act of becoming one flesh involves much more than sex. It involves merging everything owned by and associated with two persons into one combined entity, with everything jointly owned and managed. What things would this include?

Property, Decisions, Financial, Raising family, Values Extended Family, Goals, mission

3. Anything that is not mutually owned and controlled by both parties will lead to division and problems. If you withhold certain possessions from your spouse, what does this communicate to him or her?

That you dont trust them

4. Among the ways that people violate this law, there are three that are primary. Those violations are dominance, selfishness, and over-protectiveness.

   - How would you define dominance?

   Controlling Force

   - How would you define selfishness?

   thinking or doing only for yourself without Regard of the affects

   - Give an example of over-protectiveness.

5. Read Luke 14:33. **How is surrendering to Christ reflected in your relationship to your spouse?**

I'm able to serve him and be obedient because its an honor instead of a matter of pride

6. There are four truths about how the Law of Possession impacts marriages:

   ■ Possessions communicate what is valued and is a priority.

   ■ Legitimate jealousy is either conquered or created by how possessions are managed.

   ■ Sharing possessions and yielding ownership builds intimacy.

   ■ Sharing possessions and yielding ownership fosters interdependence.

To what possessions do you think these truths apply?

Finances, Houses, Cars

7. There are practical ways to establish this law in your marriage.

   ■ Ask your spouse to pray with you about the decisions in your marriage.

   ■ Never make a significant decision without your spouse (and be sure you agree on what is "significant").

   ■ Communicate regularly your willingness to share possessions if it becomes an issue with your spouse.

In what ways do the suggestions above establish the Law of Possession in a marriage?

RELATE AND COMMUNICATE

1. Look again at the list of possessions you wrote during the opening activity. If you identified any items using "my" or "mine," what does that reflect about your attitude towards that item?

2. If you insist on your independence and "personal rights," what will happen to real intimacy in your relationship?

3. Give an example (not a personal example) of how a husband might be dominant in one area and how a wife might control a different area.

4. Give an example of a time when yielding a possession brought about a deeper sense of intimacy.

WRAP IT UP

Intimacy is not built solely or primarily on great sex or deep conversations. True intimacy is created when two people so intertwine their lives with one another that one cannot determine where one life ends and the other begins. If a spouse refuses to surrender ownership of anything—including time, money, children and energy—it will create resentment and legitimate jealousy and can eventually destroy or severely damage the relationship.

TALK IT OUT
Find a location away from other couples for privacy.

1. Take a moment to reflect and write the answers to these questions:

   ■ What, if anything, do I have difficulty sharing with my spouse?

   ■ Concerning the "division of labor" or "chores" in our relationship, is there any work that I need to learn to share so that we can manage our marriage together?

2. Share the answers above with your spouse and then listen, without criticizing, to what your spouse shares with you.

3. Pray with your spouse, asking God to open your heart to be able to trust your spouse with everything you have.

4. Before you leave this evening, set a time and place for you and your spouse to complete the homework session before we meet again.

OUR TIME
Date_____ Time _____

Place _____

WALK IT OUT

Before your time together, review chapter five of Marriage on the Rock.

Begin by praying with each other and then share the following:

- How does it make you feel when your spouse controls or dominates in an area? Focus only on your feelings and not on placing blame.

- What has worked for you in the past to help you be less selfish and better share everything with each other?

Now spend a few minutes meditating on the following topics. Determine your views on how selfish or dominant you feel you may be in each of these areas.

- Time

- Money

- Decision-making

- Chores

- Activity choices

Share your insights from the above questions with your spouse. If you see any problem areas, brainstorm some specific changes you could make together to move towards sharing all things.

For next week, read chapter six in *Marriage on the Rock.*

NOTES...

THE LAW
OF PURITY

God designed marriage to function in an atmosphere of purity between a husband and wife–a safe, secure atmosphere so that each one is free to share personal feelings and vulnerabilities with the other.

REVIEW

Share a few new ideas that you and your spouse came up with to help you fulfill the law of possession in your marriage.

GET STARTED

Who Does It Affect?

Each of you take the glass of water that your leader has supplied. This glass of water represents you. Put a spoonful of dirt into one glass so that each couple has one glass of clean water and one of dirty. Now mix both glasses together. What happened to the water that had no dirt in it? How is this like the effect of each person's behavior on the marriage?

DISCOVER TRUTH

The fourth and final law of marriage is from Genesis 2:25, "The man and his wife were both naked and were not ashamed."

Think again about the water you mixed in the opening activity.

1. Do you believe it is possible for a person to have hidden sin that does not affect his or her spouse? no – all Can or will affect others at Same time

Reading for this session...

Read Chapter six of *Marriage on the Rock*

notes:

2. Adam and Eve's relationship, before their choice to sin, was God's picture of a perfect marriage.

  - What was their condition in the beginning?

  no Shame - Fully "naked" baring all to each other in mind, Body & Soul

3. God intended marriage to be a place of total "nakedness." Adam and Eve shared themselves completely—physically, mentally, emotionally, and spiritually—in an atmosphere of intimacy and openness, with each other and with God.

  - Discuss how Adam and Eve were "naked" in each of these four areas.

4. Before Adam and Eve experienced sin:

  - Their differences could be openly expressed (the genitals being completely uncovered revealed one of the several differences they had).

  - They could have unhindered intimacy (no "covering" to interfere with their intimacy).

  - Their most sensitive areas could be exposed without fear (the genitals are the most sensitive area of the body).

  Read Genesis 3:6–10. How were each of the three areas listed above affected when Adam and Eve sinned? *They became aware of Sin AND immediately was Shame of their nakedness giving into fear - Shame - Hiding*

5. Read Romans 6:23. What is the penalty for sin?

Death

6. When we allow sin into our lives, no matter how small, we swallow a deadly poison. We become open targets for Satan's lies and destructive schemes. There is no such thing as a private sin. Because of this, a spouse has a right to be concerned about every area of his or her partner's life.

   ■ How many entry points or "strongholds" in a person's marriage or personal life does Satan need to destroy a marriage? *Just one small opening or tear in your marriage*

7. Read 1 Peter 5:8. The best way to keep the end result of sin from occurring in your marriage is to stop it in the beginning. If sin has already crept in, the redeeming grace of God makes it possible to restore an atmosphere of purity in your relationship, no matter what the sin. These are the steps for creating or restoring an atmosphere of purity:

   ■ First, take responsibility for your own behavior. Read Luke 6:41–42. How does this verse apply to marriage?

   ■ Do not deal with a sinful situation by retaliating in sin. Although 1 Peter 3:1–2 is written to wives, the principle applies to both spouses—you must commit to using purity when you are addressing problems. Never practice sinful revenge or retaliation when you are confronting your spouse.

   ■ It is vital to confess your faults. 1 John 1:9 and James 4:6 and 5:16 all point out the power of confessing your faults. Even if your spouse doesn't reciprocate or respond positively, you must admit your mistakes so that you will be right before God.

- Extend forgiveness. What does Jesus say in Matthew 6:14–15 about forgiveness? The poison of unforgiveness damages the vessel it is stored in worse than it hurts the one to whom it is directed. Even if you are forgiving of your spouse, unforgiveness toward others in your life will still yield resentment and bitterness that will harm your marriage.

- Finally, it is important to pray with and for each other and to surround yourselves with people who will encourage you to seek God and love your spouse. You don't need friends who will seduce you into sin. What does 1 Corinthians 15:33 teach about the type of company you should keep?

RELATE AND COMMUNICATE

1. Share how God has helped you to overcome sin in other areas of your life and discuss some victories that you have experienced in your marriage.

   Allowing God to work/ Cut my Pride issues and allow myself to be open in Love & Honesty AND being able to expose myself AND be vulnerable to accept Love AND Not be afraid and to trust in God AND Honor your spouse

2. Based on Luke 6:41–42 what type of God–inspired behavior can you practice to encourage your spouse to respect and trust you? *Being honest and open. AND accept & Honor your partner even when they may fail*

3. Why is it dangerous to allow hurts and frustrations in your relationship to build up rather than dealing with them openly and honestly? *It can cause resentment and you can start withdrawing from the relationship to AVOID hurts or fights*

4. What characteristics would you seek in friends who will be a positive influence on your marriage?

encouragement that follows Gods word
Joyfulness in their own relationships
non-Judging attitude
Honest approach of Life

WRAP IT UP

God designed marriage to function in an atmosphere of purity. As long as the marriage partners have not sinned against one another, they can feel comfortable exposing themselves to each other physically, emotionally, and spiritually. When one spouse damages the other, the injured spouse will naturally try to protect his or her differences and sensitivities.

The solution is for the sinning or offending spouse to ask for forgiveness and to begin making changes to restore trust. When that has been done and purity has been restored, the two can be open to one another again.

TALK IT OUT

Find a location away from other couples for privacy.

1. Take a moment to reflect and write the answers to these questions:

   - Of the four areas of openness—physical, emotional, mental and spiritual—which is your spouse most comfortable exhibiting?

     Physical & Sometimes emotional

   - In which of these four areas do you need to improve in your willingness to be open?

     Spiritual & emotional

2. Share your answers with your spouse, and be sure to communicate in love and humility.

3. Pray with your spouse, thanking God that He has provided forgiveness of all your sins. Ask for His help in extending that same forgiveness to your spouse.

4. Before you leave this evening, set a time and place for you and your spouse to complete the homework session before we meet again.

OUR TIME
*Date*_____ *Time* _____

Place _____

WALK IT OUT
Before your time together, review chapter six in *Marriage on the Rock*.

Begin by praying for each other and, using the speaker/learner technique from session 3, share with each other the following:

- Something your spouse does that makes you want to hide (protect) yourself.

- What do you think you could do and your spouse could do to improve the situation?

Now take a personal inventory of areas where you are not being completely honest with your spouse. Review the steps to restore purity to your marriage, and read again the Bible verses upon which they are based. The steps are listed below:

- Take responsibility for your own behavior. (Romans 6:23)

- Do not return sin for sin. (Luke 6:27–36)

- Admit your faults. (1 John 1:9, James 4:6 and 5:16)

- Forgive by releasing your spouse from personal judgment and by yielding your right of retaliation or punishment. (Matthew 6:14–15, Hebrews 12:15)

Husbands, take your wives' hands in yours and verbally commit to provide an atmosphere of purity and safety for your wife. Wives, make the same commitment to your husbands.

For next week, read chapters seven and thirteen in *Marriage on the Rock*.

NOTES...

THE FOUR BASIC NEEDS
OF A MAN

A man needs honor and respect, sexual fulfillment, companionship, and support at home.

REVIEW

How has the atmosphere of purity and trust changed in your marriage in the last few weeks?

GET STARTED

Vive la Difference!

In the following chart, fill out the areas where you and your mate differ. Frame your answers with positive language. Being different does not mean that one is right and one is wrong; it means every person is unique.

AREA	ME	SPOUSE
Approach to physical intimacy		
Style of communicating		
Recreational wants		
Help around the house		

SESSION 8

Reading for this session...

This session is based on chapters seven and thirteen of *Marriage on the Rock*.

notes:
_____
_____
_____
_____
_____
_____
_____
_____
_____
_____
_____
_____
_____
_____
_____
_____
_____
_____
_____
_____

DISCOVER TRUTH

Read Ephesians 5:22–33 carefully. According to verse 33:

1. What does God require of husbands?

2. What does God require of wives?

3. Many people resist making changes in their own lives that will affect their marriages in positive ways. Sometimes people don't want to be the first one in the marriage to start making changes because they are fearful that they will be rejected or be taken advantage of and become vulnerable. Another reason people resist changing their behavior is because they may have been strongly influenced by the world and have a perverted view of marriage roles. Often it is simply a lack of belief that biblical principles really work.

   ■ What would be the result of someone refusing to make needed changes in the way they respond to their spouse?

4. Many people have a hard time accepting the truth that there are basic, God-created differences between men and women which result in natural differences of behavior and needs. As a result, people spend time trying to change their spouses, instead of accepting how God created them and focusing on improving the marriage relationship.

   ▪ What would be an example of a God-created difference between men and women?

5. Another challenge to a healthy relationship is that one can mistakenly translate a spouse's needs into his or her own language or manner of communicating. For example, when a wife says she wants affection, her husband may think she wants sex. Conversely, when a husband says he wants sex, his wife may think he really just needs non-sexual affection.

   ▪ How would the inaccurate translation of a spouse's need affect the marriage relationship?

The relationship needs of men and women vary greatly. In this session we will look at the four strongest relationship needs of a man. Next week we will focus on the four strongest needs of a woman.

6. Every man, regardless of personality, has four primary needs. They are honor and respect, sexual fulfillment, companionship and domestic support. Honor is a man's greatest need. Ephesians 5:22 and 33b are both addressed to the wife about her husband's need for honor and respect.

   ■   What are some practical ways a wife can demonstrate honor and respect to her husband?

7. The second need of a man is sexual fulfillment. Sex is a powerful force in a man's life, and the wife is God's only legitimate resource for satisfying the husband's needs. When a wife rejects her husband's need for sex, she is rejecting him because his sexual drive is an essential part of who he is. The wife must understand the strength and importance of the male appetite and need for sex.

   ■   How would not meeting your husband's sexual needs leave him vulnerable?

8. A woman is put in touch with her sexuality through her emotions, but a man is put in touch with his emotions through sex. It is important for the wife to understand and embrace her husband's need for visual and physical stimulation. A woman needs to give her husband the visual satisfaction he needs. Physical exposure can sometimes be uncomfortable for the wife.

   ■   What are some reasons a wife might have difficulty in fulfilling her husband's visual stimulation needs?

9. Companionship is another important need for a man. Initially, a couple falls in love while having fun together and enjoying each other's company. A man has a continuing need for that same kind of companionship—for his wife to continue relating to him as his best friend. A wife needs to make an effort to be involved in fun activities that her husband enjoys.

   ■ How would being involved in activities together deepen intimacy?

10. Finally, the last need for a man is domestic support. A woman can meet her husband's need for domestic support—having a place of belonging—by making their home a place where the husband loves to be. This does not mean the wife should handle all the domestic responsibilities but that her instincts for making a "house a home" need to come to the forefront.

   ■ What are some ways a "house" can be a "home"?

RELATE AND COMMUNICATE

1. Give an example of how making a change in yourself affected the marriage in a positive way.

2. Where might a man seek honor and respect outside the marriage relationship when it is not given by his wife?

3. How does a wife's submission, as discussed in Ephesians 5:22–33, work together with the sacrificial love that is required by the husband in those verses?

4. Give two examples of how a couple might mistakenly translate their spouse's needs into their own language.

WRAP IT UP

As a woman commits to be the best wife she can and to meet her husband's needs for honor, sex, companionship, and domestic support, and her husband commits to meeting her needs, with God's help they can begin to experience a dream marriage.

TALK IT OUT

Find a location away from other couples for privacy.

1. Take a moment to reflect and write the answers to these questions:

    - What did you and your spouse have fun doing when you were dating or courting?

    - In what activities that you do now do you enjoy each other's company?

2. Share the answers from above with each other and decide on one or more activities you could try doing again.

3. Pray with your spouse. Wives, pray for your husbands, thanking God for them. Ask for God's help to learn to love and honor your spouse and to meet his needs.

4. Before you leave this evening, set a time and place for you and your spouse to complete the homework session before we meet again.

OUR TIME

*Date*_____ *Time* _____

Place _____

WALK IT OUT

Before your time together, review chapters seven and thirteen in *Marriage on the Rock*.

Begin by praying with each other and then share the following:

- In what ways have you or your spouse mistranslated each other's needs into your own language?

- What are some of the most notable differences between you as man and woman?

- How can these differences strengthen you as a team?

Now spend some time answering the following questions, focusing on changes you can make in your behaviors that will have a positive effect on the marriage.

HUSBANDS

1. In what ways does your wife do a good job of making you feel honored and respected? What things could she do to make you feel more honored and respected?

2. Remember a very romantic experience you had together that truly met your sexual needs. How could you work with your wife to recreate that type of experience?

WIVES

1. What do you truly admire and respect about your husband? How could you do a better job of communicating that to your husband?

2. Remember a truly romantic experience the two of you had together. Think back to what made your husband feel that you cared about his sexual needs. How could you work on expressing that to him again?

Share your answers with each other. Focus on yourself—your own behaviors—and commit to make changes in yourself for the sake of building a dream marriage.

For next week, read chapter ten in *Marriage on the Rock*.

NOTES...

THE FOUR BASIC NEEDS
OF A WOMAN

REVIEW

Share how you were able to communicate honor to each other and to establish more romance in your relationship.

GET STARTED

A Rose by any Other Name

Look at the flower that the leader has provided. What does this flower need in order to thrive? How are the flower's needs similar to what a woman needs from her husband to thrive and grow?

DISCOVER TRUTH

Just as a man has special needs, so does a woman. A man who loves his wife and wants to build a good marriage will do his best to understand and meet his wife's needs.

Let's review Ephesians 5:22–33 again. This time we will focus on verses 25–30.

1. Who is the example for men to follow in loving their wives?

SESSION 9

Reading for this session...

This session is based on chapter ten of *Marriage on the Rock*.

notes:

2. What did Christ do to show His love for the church?

3. So what must a man do to show his love for his wife?

4. Despite being very difficult to define, security is a woman's greatest need. There are four powerful ways a man can meet this need for security in his wife. The first way is a reflection of the law of priority: a man must communicate that he cares for his wife more than he cares for anyone or anything. He needs to be totally committed to meeting her needs, regardless of what it costs him.

    ■   What fears might keep a man from making this level of commitment to his wife?

5. The second practical way to meet a woman's need for security is for the husband to communicate his admiration and love for his wife. A husband needs to praise his wife every day, being sincere in what he communicates. Every area of his wife's life should be praised.

    ■   In what areas of a woman's life could her husband compliment and show his pride in her?

6. The third powerful way a man can build security in his wife's life is by communicating his faithfulness. Read Matthew 5:28.

- What types of activities must a husband be sure to avoid in order to maintain his faithfulness to his wife?

- This type of commitment to sexual purity on a husband's part will provide the security his wife needs in order to blossom—to be free and responsive in the bedroom. Faithfulness also requires that a husband never use the words *divorce* or *leave*. The possibility of divorce brings real insecurity for the wife.

- Why is using the word *divorce* so destructive?

7. The fourth way a husband can build security in his wife is by communicating his dedication to provide for the family financially. This involves praying for God's blessing and direction, aggressively seeking the best employment possible, being a hard and faithful worker, and being a wise money manager.

- In what ways might a husband affect his wife's sense of security through his attitude towards work?

8. The next basic need of a woman is for nonsexual, soft affection. It can be very challenging for some men to show nonsexual touch, but often, when a wife's need for this type of touch is met, she becomes much more responsive sexually.

   ■ What are some examples of nonsexual, affectionate touching?

9. The third need a woman has is for open communication with her husband. Think back to the session on communication.

   ■ Describe how a husband can have open communication with his wife.

10. The last deep need of a woman is for leadership. The husband's role as leader in the home has at times been misunderstood and abused by men in the past. Reread Ephesians 5:25–33. The kind of leadership a woman wants from her husband is that of a sacrificial, servant leader—a leader whose primary concern is the uplifting and building up of his wife. This kind of leadership from a husband naturally leads to a trusting submission from his wife.

   ■ In what areas of life does a husband need to demonstrate leadership?

RELATE AND COMMUNICATE

1. Give an example of a time when feeling secure has made an impact on your life. This could be in a job situation, in your marriage, or in your Christian life.

2. How do expressions of soft, nonsexual affection from a husband make his wife feel more loved?

3. In what ways could a couple establish more detailed communication in their daily interactions?

4. What are the dangers of a man becoming dominant in his leadership of the family? What are the benefits of sacrificial leadership?

WRAP IT UP

Think once more about the flower that you examined earlier. A flower can bring blessing and joy to a home. So can a woman whose needs are being met by her husband. Husbands and wives both need to understand what it takes to make a woman thrive and bloom.

TALK IT OUT

Find a location away from other couples for privacy.

1. Take a moment to reflect and write the answers to these questions:

   ■ What kinds of soft, nonsexual affection can you begin adding to your relationship?

   ■ How can you achieve a greater sense of security in your marriage?

2. Share your answers from above, and commit to implementing some of the behaviors you discussed.

3. Pray with your spouse. It would be especially powerful for the husband to pray for his wife, asking God for His help in better understanding her needs and in learning how to meet those needs.

4. Before you leave this evening, set a time and place for you and your spouse to complete the homework session before we meet again.

OUR TIME

*Date*_____ *Time* _____

Place _____

WALK IT OUT

Before your time together, review chapter ten in *Marriage on the Rock.*

Begin by praying together and then share the following:

- What principles from the Ephesians 5:22–33 passage do you feel you are applying well in your marriage?

- Which of the four needs of a woman may need to be addressed in your marriage?

Now spend some time brainstorming ways these needs could be better met in your marriage.

WIVES

1. In what ways is your husband doing a good job of making you feel secure and loved? What things could he do to make you feel more secure and loved?

2. How does your husband show servant leadership in your marriage? In what areas would you like to see him take on more leadership?

HUSBANDS

1. In what ways do you feel you are doing a good job of providing for your family? What other things can you do to make your wife feel more secure?

2. In what ways have you met your wife's need for nonsexual affection? What types of soft, nonsexual affection are you willing to begin doing to express your love for your wife?

Share your answers with one another. Focus on your own behaviors and commit to making the sacrifice to meet each other's needs.

For next week, read chapter eighteen in *Marriage on the Rock.*

NOTES...

PRINCIPLES OF FINANCIAL SUCCESS

By working together and making wise decisions, a couple can manage their money effectively and strengthen their marriage in the process.

REVIEW

Share one way you have met your spouse's needs this week.

GET STARTED

Where Does It Go?

As a couple, determine what percentage of your monthly income is spent on each category listed below. Total percentage for all categories must not exceed 100%.

Food	_____%	Savings	_____%
Housing	_____%	Taxes	_____%
Transportation	_____%	Medical	_____%
Tithe	_____%	Clothing	_____%
Debts	_____%	Entertainment	_____%
Insurance	_____%	Miscellaneous	_____%

DISCOVER TRUTH

A large percentage of people who divorce cite conflict over money as a primary cause of their breakup. It is crucial that couples learn to handle money effectively. God clearly gives many principles in His word about our attitudes towards money.

1. Read Psalm 24:1. What principle do you find here?

SESSION 10

Reading for this session...

This session is based on chapter eighteen of *Marriage on the Rock*.

notes:

_____

_____

_____

_____

_____

_____

_____

_____

_____

_____

_____

_____

_____

_____

_____

_____

_____

_____

_____

_____

2. Read Malachi 3:8–12. These verses talk about the principle of tithing. What does this illustrate about God's blessings if we determine to hold tightly to the amount of money we have?

3. Another biblical principle is found in 1 Timothy 6:8–10. Read this passage.

    ■ What does it mean to be content?

There are four areas, or dangers, that couples face when it comes to money. These areas are: disrespect for the other spouse's financial input, domination of the couple's financial decisions by one spouse, disagreement about finances, and debt.

4. In almost every marriage, each spouse tends to view money differently. Kenneth Doyle, a financial psychologist, has identified four "money languages."[1] The first of these languages is the "driver," who equates money with success. Unless *drivers* are financially successful, they do not feel successful in life. Next is the "analytic," who equates money with security. When *analytics* have savings and budgets they adhere to, they feel safe. Third is the "amiable," who equates money with love. *Amiables* see money as a venue for showing love and care. Lastly, there is the "expressive" who equates money with acceptance and respect. Those who speak the language of the *expressive* see finances as a way to have others respect them.

    ■ How could the fact that a husband and wife have different money languages negatively influence their respect for one another's financial input?

[1] Kenneth O. Doyle, *The Social Meaning of Money and Property: In Search of a Talisman,* 1999 SAGE Publications.

5. The second area of danger in finances for a couple is that of financial dominance. There is very rarely any reason for one partner to independently control the money in a marriage. Couples must learn to communicate trust and to cooperate in the area of finances.

- What are some attitudes that might prevent couples from working together in the area of finances?

6. The third area of danger for couples is disagreements about finances. These disagreements can be kept to a minimum by having a budget. Budgets help you make financial decisions in advance by forcing you to discuss and agree on values, priorities and personal preferences in finances. Budgeting provides a basis for accountability. Conflict is much more manageable with a budget in place since you are proactive rather than reactive.

- What do you think are the steps to setting up a budget?

7. Finally, debt presents a great danger to marriage finances. It is vital that a couple live within their means and be able to put money into savings each month. Sometimes it may be necessary to downsize to be able to pay off debt. Borrowing must be reserved for those items that appreciate in value, such as real estate, rather than those items that depreciate in value, such as cars. In difficult situations, seek financial or debt counseling. There are now many organizations that offer programs to help families plan a way to get out of debt.

- What are some reasons so many couples get into trouble with debt?

RELATE AND COMMUNICATE

1. Give an example of when God has brought blessing to your life when you have been generous in your giving.

2. In what areas of your life are you experiencing contentment?

3. What do you think your financial language might be?

4. In what ways does having a budget eliminate conflict in a marriage?

WRAP IT UP

There are four foundations of financial success in a marriage:

- Honor your spouse and respect his or her differences and perspectives.

- Make all financial decisions together.

- Pray together about your finances.

- Plan a yearly budget and long-range goals—including goals for being careful about debt and living within your means.

TALK IT OUT

Find a location away from other couples for privacy.

1. Take a moment to reflect and write the answers to the following questions:

    ▪ Tell about a time when you had fun with your spouse without spending money.

    ▪ How do you think you and your spouse are doing at handling your money and making financial decisions?

2. Share your answers from the questions above, and commit to improving in the area of finances in your marriage.

3. Pray with your spouse to the One who owns the cattle on a thousand hills. Ask God to lead you to honor Him with your finances and to free you from worry and stress in this area.

4. Before you leave this evening, set a time and place for you and your spouse to complete the homework session before we meet again.

OUR TIME

*Date*_____   *Time* _____

Place _____

WALK IT OUT

Before your time together, review chapter eighteen in *Marriage on the Rock*.

Begin by praying with each other and sharing with each other answers to the following:

- Which of the "money languages" do you feel fits you, and what do you believe are your strengths and weaknesses?

- Do you think you are carrying any debt in your marriage that you shouldn't be? What can you do to reduce your debt load?

Now spend some time carefully deciding the following:

1. Take a sheet of paper and write two percentages (one for each spouse) to indicate the balance of control over the finances in your marriage. If one spouse has complete control, the percentages would be 100% and 0%.

2. How has the balance of control over finances in your marriage positively or negatively influenced your relationship with each other?

3. Begin to pray about your finances and use the "Budgeting Worksheet" to help you set new budgeting goals.

Share your answers with each other. Decide on some changes you and your spouse can implement to improve your financial situation.

For next week, read chapter twenty in *Marriage on the Rock.*

NOTES...

SEXUAL FULFILLMENT
IN MARRIAGE

God created sex for pleasure and lifelong enjoyment in marriage.

REVIEW
Share what changes you are making in the area of finances.

GET STARTED
Fire Safety
Think of all the benefits we receive from fire such as warmth, light, and beauty. Now imagine the devastating effects of a fire raging out of control. Sexuality is very similar to a fire. When we follow the guidelines God has established for sex, we experience deep levels of intimacy, communication, and fulfillment. However, if sex moves out of God's parameters, it yields destruction and death.

DISCOVER TRUTH
Sex is God's idea and His gift to married couples. It is not, as some think, inherently "dirty." Satisfying sex, however, is found only within God's parameters.

1. When you give a gift to someone, how do you feel as you see that person enjoy and appreciate the gift?

SESSION 11

Reading for this session...

This session is based on chapter twenty of *Marriage on the Rock*.

notes:

2. Just as you get pleasure from seeing someone enjoy a gift from you, so God wants married couples to enjoy giving the gift of sex to each other. However, God has established biblical parameters to protect His created design for sexual joy.

These are the seven sexual practices that God forbids:
- Sex outside of marriage: adultery, fornication

- Sex relations with a member of the same sex: homosexuality

- Sex relations with a member of your family: incest

- Sex relations with animals: bestiality

- Sex fantasies or desires for someone other than your spouse, which amounts to adultery in God's sight; pornography of any kind, as well as mentally playing out lustful fancies for real or imaginary women or men

- Sex that finds pleasure in pain or violence: rape, sadomasochism, brutality

- Sex that involves body parts not designed by God for intercourse: sodomy, anal sex

Therefore, the three basic criteria for fulfilling sex is:
- It should be consensual.

- It should be safe.

- It should enhance the relationship.

3. Read 1 Corinthians 10:23. How can the principle found in this verse be applied to sexuality in marriage?

4. Unfortunately, the process of achieving the kind of satisfaction and pleasure God intended can be frustrating. God created men and women vastly different in sexual design and sexual response. Until a couple accepts and affirms these differences and commits to sacrificially meet the sexual needs of their mate, the goal of a wonderful sex life will remain elusive.

- What are some of the differences between men and women in the area of sexual design and sexual response?

5. One of the differences that often causes difficulties for couples is that men are visually stimulated and women are emotionally stimulated. In addition, men are also more quickly aroused and ready for sex, whereas women need time and emotional connection to become ready for sex. It has been said that in the area of sexual arousal, men are like microwaves and women are like crock pots.

   - How would a lack of understanding of these differences in sexual arousal cause difficulties for a couple?

6. Another difference is the fact that men tend to compartmentalize sex and other areas of their lives, while women integrate sex with all of life. To illustrate this, women usually cannot separate what happened at breakfast this morning from sex tonight. However, a man can come home after the worst possible day, knowing tomorrow will be the end of the world, and still be able to put his full attention on sex.

   - What would be a good example of how a man compartmentalizes his life?

7. Men prefer more direct sexual stimulation, while women desire nonsexual touching and limited direct sexual stimulation. Closely related to this difference is how men see sex as an event and women see sex as a relational expression.

   - What should a husband do to meet his wife's needs, and what should a wife do to meet her husband's needs?

8. Lastly, it is important to remember that sexual stimulation causes men to be more emotionally responsive. Women, however, are sexually responsive to emotional connection.

- What could a husband do to build emotional connectedness with his wife?

- What could a wife do to help her husband identify his emotions?

9. Even when both people in a marriage are educated about differences in sexual design, there can still be some barriers to sexual fulfillment. One major barrier is pornography in any form—soft, hard, printed, Internet or video. The products of today's sex industry encourage men and women to use their spouses rather than love them. Pornography also drives a person to selfishly satisfy their own lusts, rather than to selflessly meet the needs of their spouse.

- Why do you think that pornography is such a widespread problem in our culture?

10. One more obstacle to sexual fulfillment is the huge negative impact of sexual abuse. There are some studies that indicate as many as fifty percent of all women have been sexually abused in some way. Although each person deals with abuse in a different manner, everyone must deal with the past so they can live successfully in the present. Abuse negatively affects every abused person's sexuality.

- What emotions and situations might prevent a person from opening up to receive healing of past abuse?

Another difficulty that hinders sexual satisfaction is guilt over past actions. Guilt can stem from past actions such as sexual experiences or abortion. The key for healing these wounds is to remember that there is no sin that the blood of Jesus cannot erase. Accepting God's forgiving grace can bring great freedom in sexuality.

RELATE AND COMMUNICATE

1. Why would God prohibit certain sexual activities?

2. Which of the many differences in sexual design do you feel is the most impacting and why?

3. *Are you aware of the resources and support systems that are available to help overcome issues of pornography?

4. Are you aware of the resources and support systems that are available to help overcome the devastating effects of past sexual abuse?

* A suggested list of resources and support systems are available on page 103.

WRAP IT UP

God created sex and has given us extensive freedom to explore and enjoy sexual intimacy within the bounds of marriage. The journey is along a path of faith, grace and service to our spouse. Within these guidelines we can have a great time!

TALK IT OUT

Find a location away from other couples for privacy.

1. Take a moment to reflect and write the answers to these questions:

   - Which of the general differences in sexual design do you see in you and your spouse?

   - What did you enjoy the most on your honeymoon?

2. Share your answers from the above questions with your spouse. What specific behaviors are you willing to change to better meet your spouse's sexual needs?

3. Pray with your spouse, thanking God for His gift of sex. Ask Him to guide you in unselfishly satisfying your mate.

4. Before you leave this evening, set a time and place for you and your spouse to complete the homework session before we meet again.

OUR TIME

Date _____ *Time* _____

Place _____

WALK IT OUT

Before your time together, review chapter twenty in *Marriage on the Rock*.

Begin by praying together and then share the following:

- What are some things that attracted you to your spouse and what makes him or her desirable to you?

- What new insights and understanding have you gained about the sexual needs of your spouse from this study?

Now spend some time carefully deciding the following:

1. When are you most free to enjoy sex?

2. On a separate sheet of paper, plan a romantic evening with your spouse. Try to plan for as many details as possible. Include dinner, dancing or whatever appeals to you. Try to think beyond what you normally do on an evening together. Then extend the romance of the evening with a night of sexual fun at home or in a hotel. Plan for your favorite intimate activities.

Share your answers and plans from above. The key here is to merge the plans and pick a date in the near future to actually carry out your plan.

For next week, look at your wedding pictures to refresh your memory of when you said your vows to each other.

NOTES...

VOW RENEWAL

This evening is a renewal of your commitment to each other and to the success of your marriage.

REVIEW
Spend time talking about the plans you made for your romantic evening

GET STARTED
Dinner or Dessert
> Focus on intimate communication with your spouse and enjoyment of his or her company.

WRAP IT UP
This is a moment to remember. This is what you as a couple have been working for through the past eleven sessions. This renewal represents a new beginning and recognition that your marriage is important and is a true covenant.

TALK IT OUT
Repeat the vows written here to your spouse as your leader says them.

SESSION 12

Reading for this session...

This session is based on chapter six of *Marriage on the Rock.*

notes:

HUSBANDS:

I surrender to the high call of being your covenant husband.

God has given you to me as a precious gift, and I receive you.

I will love you, nourish you and cherish you with my words and actions.

I will serve you and humbly lead you as I treat you with respect as my equal.

I will be sensitive to you as I would my own body and will diligently provide for you.

I will meet your needs and the needs of our family in a sacrificial manner, according to the model of Jesus Christ.

I commit to sexual purity and to keep myself unto you alone so long as we both shall live.

I surrender my selfish rights and assume my full responsibilities.

In spite of circumstances or emotions, as I stand against any person or force that would come to divide us, I will love you until death separates us.

I will not turn my heart away from you because of anger, difficult times, laziness, the distraction of other demands, desires or anything else.

I will work on our marriage and seek to grow as a husband and as a man of God.

With God as my witness, I vow to be your covenant husband.

_____   _____

Signature   Date

WIVES:

I surrender to the high call of being your covenant wife.

God has given you to me as a precious gift, and I receive you.

I will love you, serve you and cherish you with my words and actions.

I will treat you with respect as I would the Lord.

I will sensitively and diligently meet your needs and the needs of our family in a sacrificial manner, according to the model of Jesus Christ.

I commit to sexual purity and to keep myself unto you alone so long as we both shall live.

I surrender my selfish rights and assume my full responsibilities.

In spite of circumstances or emotions, as I stand against any person or force that would come to divide us, I will love you until death separates us.

I will not turn my heart away from you because of anger, difficult times, laziness, the distraction of other demands, desires or anything else.

I will work on our marriage and seek to grow as a wife and as a woman of God.

With God as my witness, I vow to be your covenant wife.

_____   _____

Signature   Date

NOTES

CONCLUSION

IN CLOSING

I want to share three more things with you, the things I always tell people as they complete a *Marriage on the Rock* study or seminar.

First, expect an attack from the enemy. Jesus said in John 10, "The enemy comes to kill, steal and destroy." Satan is the enemy; he doesn't want your marriage to succeed, and he will do whatever he can to spoil it. When you are working on your marriage, the devil notices—but God notices too! It is important to trust in the Lord: *"Greater is He that is in you than he that is in the world"* (1 John 4:4). Your family does have a great future, because you are precious to God.

My second piece of advice is that you should focus on yourself. It can be difficult to hear marriage advice without paying attention to what your spouse should be doing. Some people will take a lesson and say, "Honey, did you hear what he said you should do?"

*The real question should be…*What do I need to change about myself to make our marriage better? Understand that God will honor the commitment that you make. Do not use this material to accuse your spouse—use this material to grow yourself. Be the first one to do the right thing. You can gain your spouse's attention by being the one who follows God's plan for marriage.

That brings us to the third and final point. Persevere—never give up, give out or give in (to the enemy). If you keep doing what is right, God will honor it. You may go through times of discouragement and you may not see a change, but God will touch the heart of your spouse when you honor Him with your actions. If you quit, the problem will not go away; it will simply be delayed or compounded.

Apply the principles of this book to your marriage and you will be on your way to building your marriage on the Rock.

Jimmy Evans

May God richly bless you!

CLOSING PRAYER:

Lord, I pray that each person who goes through this study and reads these materials will apply the principles learned to their own life and marriage. I pray that each person will take these principles and use them properly. Let the desire to build a strong marriage lead husbands and wives to work together in humility, sacrifice and love. Lord, I pray that marriages are healed and strengthened and that You are glorified.

STAY
CONNECTED

Pass your workbooks around the room, and have each couple write their names, phone numbers, and e-mail addresses.

NAME	PHONE	E-MAIL

RESOURCES

MarriageToday™ Website . . . . www.marriagetoday.com

Rapha Christian Counseling 800-383-4673

Crisis Pregnancy Centers . . . . www.cpclink.com

American Family Association . . . . www.afa.net/pornography – 662-844-5036

New Life Ministries. . . . . www.newlife.com – 1-800-NEW LIFE (800-639-5433)

Pure Life Ministries . . . . www.purelifeministries.org – 800-635-1866

Pure Intimacy . . . . www.pureintimacy.org

Setting Captives Free . . . . www.settingcaptivesfree.com

Enough is Enough . . . . www.enough.org

Christian Men's Network . . . . www.edcole.org/resources

Crown Financial Ministries –
founder Larry Burkett. . . . . www.crown.org – (800) 722-1976

LEADERS NOTES

LEADER'S NOTES OVERVIEW

These notes have been provided to help the group leaders prepare for each session. The categories within the Leader's Notes are as follows:

Objectives

The purpose of the Objectives is to help focus on the issues that will be presented in each session.

Notes and Tips

This section will relate any general comments about the session, including a list of materials you will need. You may want to create a checklist of these materials before each session along with a list of what you hope to accomplish by the end of each session.

As a quick note—an additional resource for use with session 12, Vow Keeper renewal certificates, are available for purchase through MarriageToday™ Resources at 1-800-380-6330, or visit online at *marriagetoday.com*. Please allow seven to ten days for delivery.

Commentary

Included in this section are notes that relate specifically to the "Discover Truth" and "Relate & Communicate" questions. Not all questions will have notes. Questions with related commentaries are designated by numbers.

SESSION ONE:
The Most Important Issue in Marriage

Objectives

- Understand the four basic needs of all humans.

- Learn that these needs can only be met through a personal relationship with Jesus Christ.

- Realize that a spouse cannot meet these four basic needs.

- Examine the difficulties that are created when a spouse is expected to meet these needs.

Notes and Tips

1. Be sure you read the commitments for this group found on page 9.

2. Each couple will need a copy of *Marriage on the Rock* and the Small Group Workbook. Ideally, each individual will have a copy of the Small Group Workbook since some activities are designed for individual responses. However, one workbook and extra paper/notebook will be sufficient to complete the class. You may also want to have extra Bibles and pens or pencils on hand.

3. Because this is the first session, make a special point to tell the group the importance of setting a special time and place to do their homework assignments. Mention that they will be held accountable for their homework each week at the beginning of the next session.

Commentary

Here is some additional information about various questions in the "Discover Truth" and "Relate & Communicate" sections. The numbers that follow correspond to the questions of the same number. If you share any of these points, be sure to do so in a manner that does not discourage discussion by making you appear to be the only one with all the right answers. Begin your comments by saying things like, "One thing I notice in this passage is…" or "I think another reason for this is…" Notes are not included for every question. Many of the questions in this study are designed so that group members will draw reflections from their own opinions and experiences.

(2.) *Acceptance* is knowing that you are loved and needed by others. *Identity* is knowing that you are a significant and special individual. *Security* is knowing that you are well protected and have the provisions that you need. *Purpose* is knowing that you have a reason for living.

(4.) These are the most common responses: *yourself, your spouse, friends, children, work, job or career, church or pastors, parents, money or material possessions.*

(5.) a) Your inner security is dependent upon someone or something you cannot predict OR
resources and abilities to meet your needs are limited.

   b) Your ability to give is dependent upon your ability to get from others.

   c) Your life is filled with an atmosphere of disappointment and frustration.

   d) Your unrealistic expectations of others create a negative atmosphere of tension in your relationship.

(6.) a) Your inner security and strength are dependent upon God, and He is totally faithful and has unlimited resources.

   b) Your ability to give flows from an inner resource available to you at all times—the Holy Spirit.

   c) Your life will be filled with an atmosphere of blessing, satisfaction and optimism.

   d) Your realistic expectations of others draw you closer to them.

SESSION TWO:
Covenant Relationship

Objectives

- Learn that covenant is foundational to understanding God's view of marriage and shapes our response to the marriage.

- Identify the key characteristics of a covenant.

- Apply covenant principles to your marriage in order to lay the foundation for a deeper, mutually fulfilling relationship.

Notes and Tips

1. You will need enough pink and blue clay or Play-Doh for each couple to have a small lump of each color.

2. You may want to have a few calculators available for the couples to calculate the number of hours in a week.

Commentary

(10.) It is important to note that Jesus gave up the right to His place at the right hand of God the Father in order to take the responsibility of making us like Himself. The couples then need to see that because their marriage is to be a covenant relationship, they too need to give up their rights and take on the responsibilities of meeting their spouse's needs.

SESSION THREE:
Principles of Positive Communication

Objectives

- Learn what the Bible says about the power of the tongue.

- Understand the effects of sowing and reaping positive and negative communication.

- Identify negative and positive seeds of communication in marriage.

- Practice speaker/learner technique of communication.

Notes and Tips

1. The leader will need to provide several types of seeds to be used by the class. These seeds can be found at most nurseries, even in the off-season. You will need: pumpkin, tomato, corn, watermelon, and sunflower seeds. You can use different varieties of seeds as long as they are clearly distinguishable and that you note the changes in the activity.

SESSION FOUR:
The Law of Priority

Objectives

- Learn the biblical model from God's law of priority and its importance in marriage relationships.

- Understand the blessing of correct priorities.

- Evaluate the priorities of life.

Notes and Tips

1. This session deals with the first of the four laws of marriage. All are based on Genesis 2:24–25. Help the couples understand that their spouses must be their highest earthly priority and that priority must be communicated in a practical way.

Commentary

(1.) The verse is divided into these parts:

"For this reason a man shall leave his father and mother;"

"...and be united with his wife;"

"...and they shall become one flesh;"

"The man and his wife were both naked, and they felt no shame."

SESSION FIVE:
The Law of Pursuit

Objectives

- Realize the great need for pursuit after marriage.

- Learn the steps to renewing passion and eliminating complacency.

- Identify ways to better pursue each other.

Notes and Tips

1. Keep the opening activity light and fun. This will set the tone for the entire lesson to be focused on the positive feelings at the beginning of the relationships.

Commentary

(2.) The false conclusion would be: "If I have to work at the relationship, I must have married the wrong person."

(3.) Other myths could include: "If my feelings towards my spouse have changed, I must have married the wrong person;" "The grass is greener on the other side of the fence;" and "If I do something nice for my spouse today, I don't have to do something nice tomorrow."

(5.) The second step is to repent.

(6.) Repent means "to turn around and go in the opposite direction."

(7.) The third step is to do the deeds you did at first.

SESSION SIX:
The Law of Possession

Objectives

- Understand the law of possession.

- Identify practical areas where possession is a major issue.

- Realize that yielding possession fosters trust and unity.

Notes and Tips

1. This session can be challenging as this discussion may bring up some areas of serious conflict. Try to have individuals focus on ways to improve their own behavior and not focus on the behavior of their spouses.

Commentary

(2.) Possessions that need to be jointly owned include property, children, sex, relationships, and time.

(3.) By withholding certain possessions, you are communicating that the possession is more important than your spouse.

(4a.) *Dominance* is defined as seizing control of something that should be common to both and not seeking the input of the other spouse.

(4b.) *Selfishness* is defined as seeking to maintain independence and control over oneself.

SESSION SEVEN:
The Law of Purity

Objectives

- Realize the need for physical, emotional, mental and spiritual openness in marriage.

- Understand that individual sin is the greatest barrier to openness.

- Identify ways to restore purity and openness in the marriage.

Notes and Tips

1. For the opening activity, each person will need a glass that is less than half-filled with water. You will also need to provide a small amount of dirt, such as potting soil, and some spoons. As soon as the activity is over, encourage the couples to help clean up from the activity.

2. The word *nakedness* is used in this lesson and should be viewed as a state of openness or complete intimacy.

Commentary

(3.) Adam and Eve had no barriers to physical intimacy. They were completely open to each other mentally and emotionally, and they were perfectly connected spiritually with each other and with God.

(4.) Their differences were covered, there were now barriers to intimacy, and the areas of their lives that were the most sensitive were no longer safe.

(7a.) Luke 6:41–42 instructs each marriage partner to focus on his or her own behavior and not the spouse's behavior.

(7d.) Matthew 6:14–15 says that if a person withholds forgiveness, God will not embrace that person with His forgiveness.

SESSION EIGHT:
The Four Basic Needs of a Man

Objectives
- Identify the four strongest needs of a man.

- Evaluate areas where these needs are not being met.

- Commit to meeting the needs of the husband.

Notes and Tips
3. In addition to the teaching on the needs of a man, the lesson begins by focusing on the importance of individuals being open to make changes in themselves.

Commentary
(6.) A woman communicates honor to her husband by verbally affirming him, allowing him to fail, covering his faults, and reflecting his strengths.

(7.) If the husband's need for sex is not met in the marriage relationship, he becomes more vulnerable to sexual temptations. Be careful to never excuse unfaithfulness in any way, but do emphasize the fact that a wife needs to meet her husband's need for sex.

    a. Some reasons that a woman might have difficulty fulfilling her husband's need for visual stimulation include: *a woman's natural modesty, her poor body image and unrealistic comparisons with women in the media.*

SESSION NINE:
The Four Basic Needs of a Woman

Objectives

- Identify the four strongest needs of a woman.

- Evaluate areas where these needs are not being met.

- Commit to meeting the needs of the wife.

Notes and Tips

1. The leader will need to provide a flower in a vase of water for the couples to examine. A single flower such as a rose will be more effective than an entire bouquet.

2. This can also be a difficult session because the concept of sacrificial leadership may be difficult for some men to embrace.

Commentary

(6.) In today's society, men are confronted daily with visual images that could lead to lustful thoughts or even a spirit of unfaithfulness. Therefore, to meet his wife's need for security he must be well grounded and secure in his relationship to Christ and understand that only Christ will meet all of his needs.

b. A husband must never threaten to leave or divorce. This kind of threat completely undermines his wife's confidence in his faithfulness.

SESSION TEN:
Principles of Financial Success

Objectives

- Understand the four dangers of money in a marriage.

- Identify individual money languages and how they impact the money management in a marriage.

- Identify some areas of personal financial stress in marriage.

- Discuss possible solutions.

Notes and Tips

Make copies of the Budgeting Worksheet on page 117, providing several copies to each couple. Give them out as part of the homework assignment for the next week.

Commentary

(1.) This is the principle that God owns everything.

(6.) There are two steps to setting up a budget. First figure out how much you bring in and how much you spend. Then come up with a plan on how to manage money spent and money received according to God's principles.

BUDGETING WORKSHEET

Our Money	Food
_____	_____
_____	_____
_____	_____
_____	

Tithe	Entertainment & Recreation
_____	_____
_____	_____
_____	

Housing	Medical
_____	_____
_____	_____

Debts	Automobile
_____	_____
_____	_____
_____	

Savings	Insurance
_____	_____
_____	

	Clothing
_____	_____
_____	_____

Taxes	Miscellaneous
_____	_____
_____	_____
_____	_____

SESSION ELEVEN:
Sexual Fulfillment in Marriage

Objectives
- Identify the key differences between men and women in the area of sexual design and response.

- Discuss how the sexual union could be more fulfilling for each spouse.

Notes and Tips
1. For this session, if possible, provide a setting for a fire to be observed by the couples. The ideal situation would be to have a burning candle or fireplace. If this is not possible, emphasize in great detail the positive effects of a fire when it is properly contained and the devastating effects that are caused by fire when it burns out of control. The point of this activity is to demonstrate that fire can be a beautiful and very helpful tool for people when properly maintained, just as sex when experienced within God's biblical guidelines leads to deep intimacy, closer communication and ultimate sexual fulfillment between a husband and wife.

2. This session deals with very intimate and sensitive issues. Be sure to guide the discussions so that no personal intimate detail is shared in the group setting.

3. Be sure to approach the subject directly, using proper anatomical terms.

Commentary
(3.) 1 Corinthians 10:23 gives the principle that everything that is permissible is not always beneficial. Therefore even though a certain sexual practice is not specifically forbidden, it must be mutually agreeable to both partners.

During the "Relate & Communicate" section, the couples will be talking about resources that help people deal with the problem areas of pornography and past sexual abuse. A suggested list of resources is available on page 103 of this workbook. However, take the time to locate resources in your local area such as Christian counselors, crisis pregnancy centers that may help women deal with past abortions, church programs and ministries, along with local Christian bookstores that would have numerous products available on a wide range of topics.

SESSION TWELVE:
Vow Renewal

Objectives

- To provide a romantic atmosphere for couples to express their commitment to a covenant relationship in their marriage.

Notes and Tips

1. Try to provide a nice romantic atmosphere. This could be done at a local restaurant, or you can hold a semi-formal candlelight dinner or dessert time in someone's home.

2. This should be a time for the couples to interact with each other and not with other couples.

*Vow Keeper renewal certificates are for use with this session. See Leader's Notes Overview section for ordering information.

Commentary

At the end of dinner or dessert, you will be asking the couples to repeat after you the vows that are in their books. Take your time, and prepare the vision that this is a moment to remember. This is what they have worked toward over the past eleven weeks. This renewal represents a new beginning and recognition that they want a true covenant marriage. Be sure the couples sign and date the form in the book or the Vow Commitment Card if you have purchased them from MarriageToday™.

Jimmy & Karen Evans

Jimmy Evans is one of America's leading authorities on family and marriage relationships. He serves as president and co-founder with is wife, Karen, of MarriageToday™, a marriage ministry and national award-winning broadcast television program.

Jimmy and Karenís passion for marriage began out of the pain and near failure of their own marriage. As they began to study and seek God's help to turn around their troubled relationship, they learned key Biblical principles allowing God to heal them and build a strong and happy marriage. Realizing there was a great need in the church to help other couples who were struggling in their marriages, Jimmy and Karen began to counsel couples and lead small group bible studies in their home. With an obvious anointing to minister to marriages, Jimmy's influence and desire continued to grow - moving from small group leader, to marriage counselor, to Senior Pastor of Trinity Fellowship Church for more than twenty-four years.

During this time, a national marriage ministry was birthed and the ministry of MarriageToday™ is now in its thirteenth year. Aired nationally to millions of homes each day, Jimmy and Karen share with viewers the practical, biblical truths to build a strong and lasting marriage.

Jimmy has authored many books and created numerous seminar and resource materials to help build and strengthen marriages. Some of his more well-known works are *Our Secret Paradise, Freedom From Your Past, The Seven Secrets for Successful Families,* and *Resolving Stress in Your Marriage.* He is a popular church and conference speaker.

Karen has been an active role model, mentoring many young women in Christian character, faith and values.

Jimmy and Karen have been married for more than 38 years and have two married children and four grandchildren.

Discover MarriageToday™

MarriageToday™, founded by Jimmy and Karen Evans, is called to establish, strengthen, save, and restore family and marriage relationships through a biblical message of healing, restoration, hope and encouragement.

We are committed to providing families with the teaching and tools they need to succeed through our TV broadcast, literature, resources, seminars and the Internet. And dedicated people are joining with us in our mission through prayer and giving. We are changing the future of our nation – one home at a time.

Find out more about MarriageToday™ at
www.marriagetoday.com

Rock Solid
PARTNERS

It's not often you get the opportunity to make your own life better while helping thousands of others at the same time. But you can do that right now by saying "yes" to becoming a Rock Solid Partner.

MarriageToday has spent years developing proven tools for healing the most shattered of relationships and for making good marriages truly great. When you say "yes" to joining the ranks of MarriageToday's Rock Solid Partners, you get the good feeling that comes from knowing you are having a powerful, positive impact on the lives of children and their parents.

You also get exclusive access to our monthly *Dream Marriage Library* resource – a bundle of topical help and insight that is already transforming relationships all over America.

MONTHLY DONTATION OPTIONS

$**14**
month
DIGITAL LIBRARY ACCESS

$**28**
month
+ MONTHLY DVD'S IN THE MAIL

$**56**
month
+ PARTNER PERKS

Your church is only as strong as its members, and your members are only as strong as the state of their marriages.

WHAT IS THE STRENGTH OF YOUR CHURCH?

Marriages everywhere are ending at an alarming rate. In your community, among your church members, and even amid your staff and leadership – marriage is under attack.

Together, we can change that trend and restore marriage to its proper priority in our society.

MarriageToday is an international ministry committed to bringing healing and hope to struggling couples and by joining us YOU can make a difference!

Choose one of five partnership levels to suit your church and receive powerful resources – from small group curriculum kits to simulcasts, live events, and more.

Launch or strengthen your church's marriage ministry
Reinforce the marriages of your pastors and church leaders

HELP US · HELP YOURSELF · HELP OTHERS

Every church needs a marriage ministry. We can help you build one.
Become a Rock Solid Church today!

CALL 866-800-3244 OR VISIT MARRIAGETODAY.COM

Marriage on the Rock

Powerful and clearly defined biblical principles in the Marriage on the Rock series will help guide and prepare you for some of the most crucial undertakings in your life, family and marriage relationships. Whether this resource is used for individual study, pre-marriage or couples counseling, small group discipleship, or churchwide marriage seminars, this dynamic teaching will transform relationships in your local community.

INCLUDED IN THIS KIT:

* 10 Sessions
* Couple's Discussion Guide
* *Marriage on the Rock* book
* Small Group Workbook with Leader's Notes
* Bonus MP3
* 25 Vow Keeper Commitment Cards
* 2 Seminar Posters

BK01H......... hardcover book

BK01 .... softcover book

SGWB01 .... small group workbook

CD011 .... 5-CD series

CK011 .... curriculum kit

DVD01........ 5-DVD series

WB01 .... couples discussion guide

to order call 1-800-380-6330

marriagetoday.com

Return to Intimacy Curriculum Kit

The Return to Intimacy Small-Group Curriculum Kit is the latest and most comprehensive teaching series by Jimmy Evans on how to build inner closeness from scratch, recapture passion and romance, and achieve the highest level of fulfillment in your marriage.

This 8-week small group study teaches couples:
* The four elements of intimacy and how to create and maintain them in marriage.
* The two most common issues that destroy marriages: Destructive anger and dominance
* The secret to restoring--- and staying in-- love.
* And much more

The Return to Intimacy Curriculum Kit includes:
* 8-session DVD series
* Leader Guide
* Downloadable Couple Guides (Unlimited)
* PLUS a free Leadership Assessment to help you make the most of your group study.

Regardless of your past experience, you can **Return to Intimacy!**

Also available on CD and DVD in a 4 session series.

CK83.......Curriculum Kit
CD83.......2-CD series
DVD83.......2-DVD series

to order call 1-800-380-6330

marriagetoday.com

Our Secret Paradise

In *Our Secret Paradise*, couples discover the healing journey of marriage that begins when two people say "I do." Through practical discussions and humorous illustrations of the ups and downs of marriage, Jimmy Evans takes readers on a journey of discovery towards the keys to a strong and beautiful marriage.

BK60 ....hardcover book
CD60 ....6-CD series
DVD60........3-DVD series

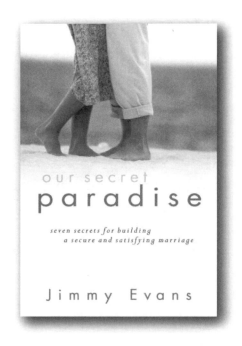

Freedom From Your Past

The past isn't really the past until it has been reconciled in Christ. Without properly addressing the pain and problems of the past, your present and future are adversely affected. In fact, many problems in relationships, emotions and attitudes are linked to unresolved issues. But here's the good news! You can find *Freedom From Your Past* by understanding and dealing with these issues in a biblical manner. You can put your past to rest. You can begin living the life of freedom God has designed for you!

BK05 . . . . . . .Book

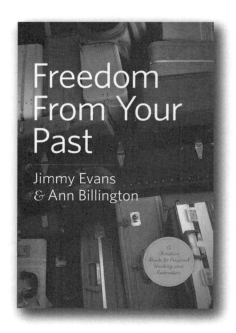

to order call 1-800-380-6330

marriagetoday.com

7 Secrets of Successful Families

At last America has a manual for successful families—*7 Secrets of Successful Families*. Discover ways to strengthen communication in your family, resolve conflict, establish priorities and implement responsibility for you and your children. These secrets will transform your family's structure, improve your ability to relate and help you overcome destructive behaviors.

BK07 .... softcover book
CD07 .... 6-CD series

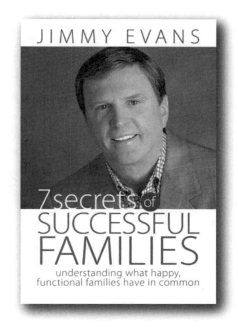

Every Great Marriage

What is a great marriage and how can a couple have one? In this teaching the roles of a husband and a wife are defined and areas of weakness are targeted that could undermine the satisfaction and success of your marriage. Jimmy Evans outlines the seven traits of every great marriage and demonstrates how you can build them into your own marriage relationship. Remember… great marriages do not happen by accident and they are not a matter of chemistry or luck, they are the result of intentional living.

CD77 . . . . . . .2-CD series
DVD77 . . . . . . .2-DVD series

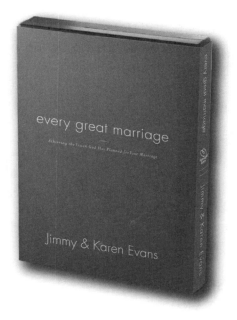

The Mountaintop of Marriage

In this powerful 40 page guidebook couples take a journey into the areas of spiritual and personal growth, preparation and vision for their family. Serving as a hands on, practical tool the information contained in this journal leads couples to address important topics such as marriage priorities and values. With thought provoking questions and a 12 month planning calendar couples can record milestone events, family accomplishments and much more while creating a family keepsake to reference for years to come.

BK13.......Book

Sex, Love & Communication

Would you believe someone who told you that God's plan for marriage includes fulfilling sex, romantic love, and healthy, vibrant communication? You should, because it's true! In this series you will learn important truths that will help you create a beautiful, passionate marriage other couples will want to imitate.

CD80.......2-CD series
DVD80.......2-DVD series